Kim Is It!

by Liza Charlesworth

ISBN: 978-1-338-84420-7

Art Director: Tannaz Fassihi; Designer: Cynthia Ng; Illustrated by Kevin Zimmer
Copyright © Liza Charlesworth. All rights reserved. Published by Scholastic Inc.

3 4 5 6 7 68 26 25 24

Printed in Jiaxing, China. First printing, June 2022.

SCHOLASTIC

Kim is a kid.
Kim has a pal.
The pal is Pig!

"I am it!" said Kim.
Then Pig ran and hid.

Pig hid in a bag.
But Pig did not fit.

4

Did Kim see him?
Yes, Kim did!

5

Dig, dig!
Dig, dig!

Pig hid in a pit.
But Pig did not fit.

Did Kim see him?
Yes, Kim did!

Pig got a big wig.

Then Pig hid
in a big box.
It had a lid.
Pig DID fit.

Did Kim see him?
Kim did NOT.

11

POP!
It is Pig in a big wig
in a big box!

"Pig, you win!" said Kim.

Read & Review

Invite your learner to point to each short-*i* word
and read it aloud.

him

hid

is

fit

pig

wig

did

kid

Kim

win

dig

in

pit

lid it big

15

Fun Fill-Ins

Read the sentences aloud, inviting your learner to complete them using the short-*i* words in the box.

> wig   it   win   pit   Pig

1. This story is about Kim and

   _____.

2. Kim said, "I am _____!"

3. Pig did not fit in the _____.

4. Pig put on a big _____.

5. At the end, Kim said:

   "Pig, you _____!"